# HAPPY SONGS

## Twenty-three of the greatest feel-good songs of *all time*

Arranged for piano, voice and guitar

Published by
**Wise Publications**
8/9 Frith Street, London W1D 3JB, UK.

Exclusive Distributors:
**Music Sales Limited**
Distribution Centre, Newmarket Road, Bury St Edmunds, Suffolk IP33 3YB, UK.

**Music Sales Pty Limited**
120 Rothschild Avenue, Rosebery, NSW 2018, Australia.

Order No. AM92233
ISBN 0-7119-4358-3
This book © Copyright 2005 Wise Publications,
a division of Music Sales Limited.

Printed in the EU.

Your Guarantee of Quality
As publishers, we strive to produce every book to the highest commercial
standards. This book has been carefully designed to minimise awkward page
turns and to make playing from it a real pleasure. Particular care has been
given to specifying acid-free, neutral-sized paper made from pulps which
have not been elemental chlorine bleached. This pulp is from farmed sustainable
forests and was produced with special regard for the environment. Throughout,
the printing and binding have been planned to ensure a sturdy, attractive
publication which should give years of enjoyment. If your copy fails to meet
our high standards, please inform us and we will gladly replace it.

**www.musicsales.com**

This publication is not authorised for sale in
the United States of America and / or Canada

**WISE PUBLICATIONS**
*part of The Music Sales Group*
London / New York / Paris / Sydney / Copenhagen / Berlin / Madrid / Tokyo

# HAPPY SONGS

# Alright

Words & Music by Gareth Coombes, Daniel Goffey & Michael Quinn

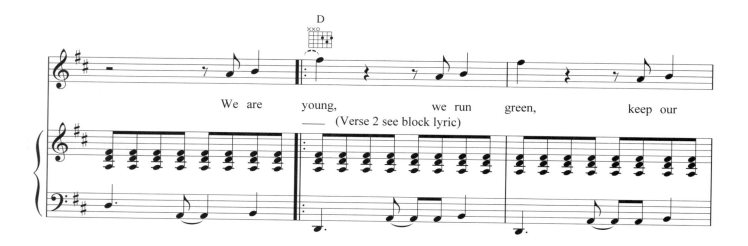

We are young, we run green, keep our
—— (Verse 2 see block lyric)

teeth nice and clean,__ see our friends, see the sights,__

feel al - right. We wake up,

we go out, smoke a fag, put it out, see our

friends, see the sights, feel al - right.

Are we like you? I can't be sure. of the scene

5

Verse 2:
But we are young, we get by
Can't go mad, ain't got time
Sleep around, if we like
But we're alright.

Got some cash, bought some wheels
Took it out 'cross the fields
Lost control, hit a wall
But we're alright.

# Build Me Up Buttercup

Words & Music by Tony Macaulay & Michael D'Abo

*Verse 2:*
You are my toy but I could be the boy you adore
If you just let me know
Although you aren't true I'm attracted to you all the more
Why do I need you so?

Baby, baby try to find *etc.*

# Brown Eyed Girl

Words & Music by Van Morrison

la la la la la la   la te da.

**VERSE 2:**
Whatever happened
To Tuesday and so slow
Going down the old mine
With a transistor radio
Standing in the sunlight laughing
Hiding behind a rainbow's wall
Slipping and a' sliding
All along the waterfall
With you, my brown eyed girl
You, my brown eyed girl.

**VERSE 3:**
So hard to find my way
Now that I'm all on my own
I saw you just the other day
My, how you have grown
Cast my memory back there Lord
Sometimes I'm overcome thinkin' 'bout it
Laughing and a' running, hey hey
Behind the stadium
With you, my brown eyed girl
You, my brown eyed girl.

# Can't Get You Out Of My Head

Words & Music by Cathy Dennis & Rob Davis

Verse 2:
There's a dark secret in me
Don't leave me locked in your heart
Set me free *etc.*

# Denis

Words & Music by Neil Levenson

moi j'ai flashe à nos deux: De - nis, De - nis,___ un grand bais - er d'é -
em - bras - se moi ce soir, De - nis, De - nis,___ un grand bais - er d'é -

-ter - ni - té.
-ter - ni - té.

Oh, De - nis, oo be doo, I'm in love with

you. De - nis, oo be doo, I'm in love with you. De - nis, oo be

27

# Don't Worry, Be Happy

Words & Music by Bobby McFerrin

C                         Dm

1. Here's a lit-tle song I wrote,    you might want to sing it note
3. Ain't got no place to lay your head,    some-bo-dy came and took
5. Ain't got no cash, ain't got no style,    ain't got no gal to make

F                         F/G

for note. Don't wor-ry,             be
your bed. Don't wor-ry,             be
you smile, but don't wor-ry,       be

C     F/G     C     F/G     C

hap-py.
hap-py.                In ev-'ry life we have
hap-py.                4. The land-lord say your rent
                                      6. 'Cos when you're wor-ried your

29

some trou - ble;     but when you wor - ry you make  it dou - ble. Don't
is late,     he may have to li - ti - gate.  Don't
face will frown,     and that will bring ev - 'ry - bo - dy down.  So don't

wor - ry,     be hap - py.
wor - ry,     be hap - py.
wor - ry,     be hap - py.

*Spoken: Don't worry, be happy now.*

*Don't worry,*

31

# Don't Stop

Words & Music by Christine McVie

# Good Vibrations

Words & Music by Brian Wilson & Mike Love

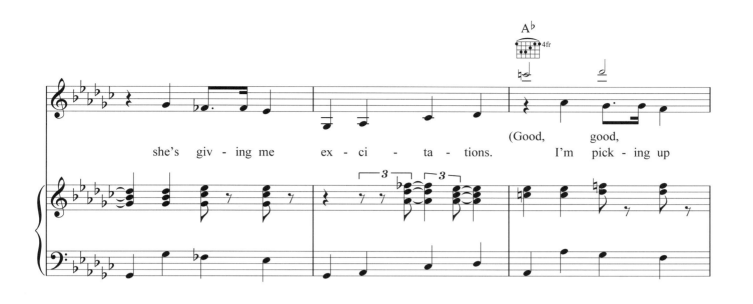

she's giv - ing me ex - ci - ta - tions. (Good, good, I'm pick - ing up

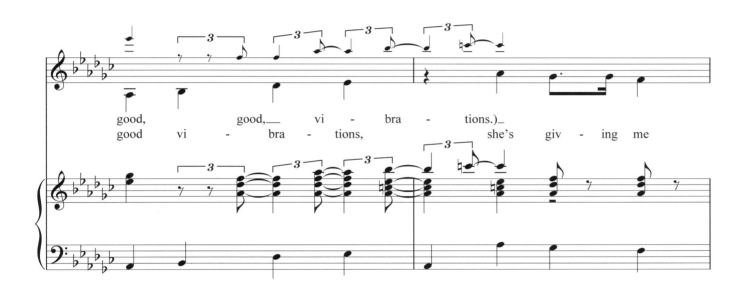

good, good, vi - bra - tions.)
good vi - bra - tions, she's giv - ing me

Good, good, good good vi - bra -
ex - ci - ta - tions. I'm pick - ing up good vi - bra - tions,

tions.)

she's giv - ing me ex - ci - ta - tions.

Ah._____          Oh,    my,__   my   one   e - la-

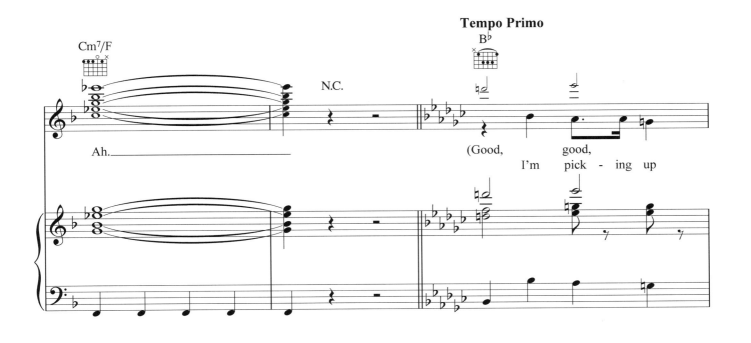

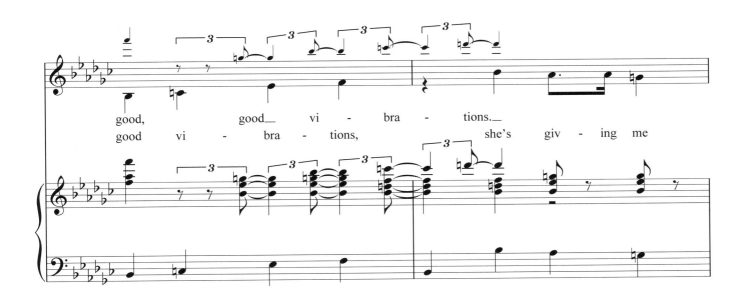

good,       good___  vi - bra - tion.___

Na,    na,  na,   na,  na,

na,   na,   na.                    Na,   na,  na,   na,  na,

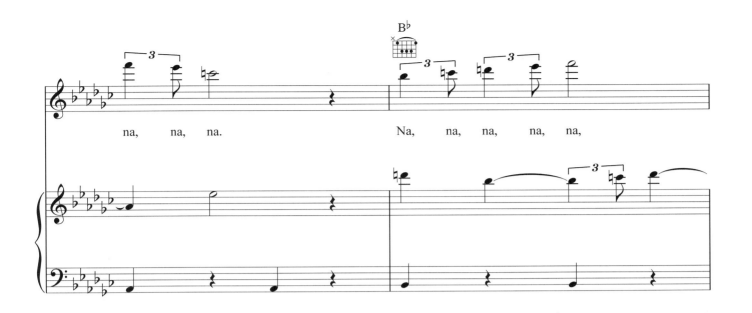

na,    na,    na.                          Na,    na,    na,    na,    na,

na,    na,    na.              Na,    na,    na,    na,    na,              na,    na,    na.

*Repeat to fade*

# Happy Together

Words & Music by Garry Bonner & Alan Gordon

1. I-ma-gine me and you; I do, I think a-bout you

day and night, it's on-ly right___ to think a-bout the girl you love and hold her

46

# Heaven Must Be Missing An Angel

Words & Music by Keni St.Lewis & Freddie Perren

51

# House Of Fun

Words & Music by Michael Barson & Lee Thompson

1. Good morn - ing Miss,      can I help you son?      Six -
(2.) of bal - loons,      with the feather - lite touch.      Pack of

55

59

# Hey Ya!

Words & Music by André Benjamin

Don't try to fight the feel - in' 'cause the thought a - lone__ is kill - ing me right now.

Thank God for Mum and Dad__ for stick - ing two to - ge - ther 'cos we don't know how.

61

Hey ya,___ hey ya.___ Hey, ya,___ Hey ya.___

You think you've got it, oh___ you think you've got it, but got it just don't get it till there's

ho - nest.      I'm   just   be - ing   ho - nest.

ya,_____   Hey___

ya._____

*See block lyric*

*Play 4 times*

Shake it    shake   shake it     shake it    shake   shake it     shake it    shake   shake it

66

shake it    shake it    shake shake it    shake it like a po-la-roid    pic - ture.    Hey ya.

Shake it    shake shake it    shake it    shake shake it    shake it    shake it    shake shake it

shake it like a po-la-roid    pic - ture.    Shake it    shake shake it    shake it    shake shake it
Now Be-yon-cè's    and Lucy Lui's,    and baby dolls, get on the floor.

shake it    shake    shake it    shake it like a    po - la - roid
You    know    what    to

Hey, alright now
Alright now fellas (YEAH!)
Now what's cooler than bein' cool?
(ICE COLD!) I can't hear ya'
I say what's cooler than bein' cool?
(ICE COLD!) whooo...
Alright, alright, alright, alright
Alright, alright, alright, alright
Alright, alright, alright, alright
Alright, alright, ok now ladies (YEAH!)
And we gon' break this thing down in just a few seconds
Now don't have me break this thing down for nothin'
Now I wanna see y'all on y'all baddest behavior
Lend me some suga', I am your neighbour, ahh here we go!

# I Got You (I Feel Good)

Words & Music by James Brown

⊕ *Coda*

So good,        so good———    since I got    you.——

So good,        so good,     since I got    you.——

**rit.**

Hey!       Oh,— yeah!

*Drums*

*Verse 2, 3 & 4:*
I feel nice, like sugar and spice
I feel nice, like sugar and spice
So nice, so nice since I got you.

*Verse 5:*
I feel good, like I knew that I would now
I feel good, I knew that I would
So good, so good since I got you.

# Love Shack

Words & Music by Fred Schneider, Kate Pierson, Cynthia Wilson & Keith Strickland

73

-'ry - bo-dy's groov-ing, ba - by. Fun-ky lit-tle shack, fun - ky lit - tle shack!

Love    Shack,    ba - by, Love___ Shack.    Bang,    bang,___    bang___

*2°/3° only*

*Play RH 2°/3° only*

*D.S. al Coda*

*Coda*

79

# Lovely Day

Words & Music by Bill Withers & Skip Scarborough

1. When I wake up in___ the morn - ing, love,___
2. 3. When the day that lies___ a - head___ of me___

84

*Repeat to fade*

# Lovin' Each Day

Words & Music by Gregg Alexander & Rick Nowels

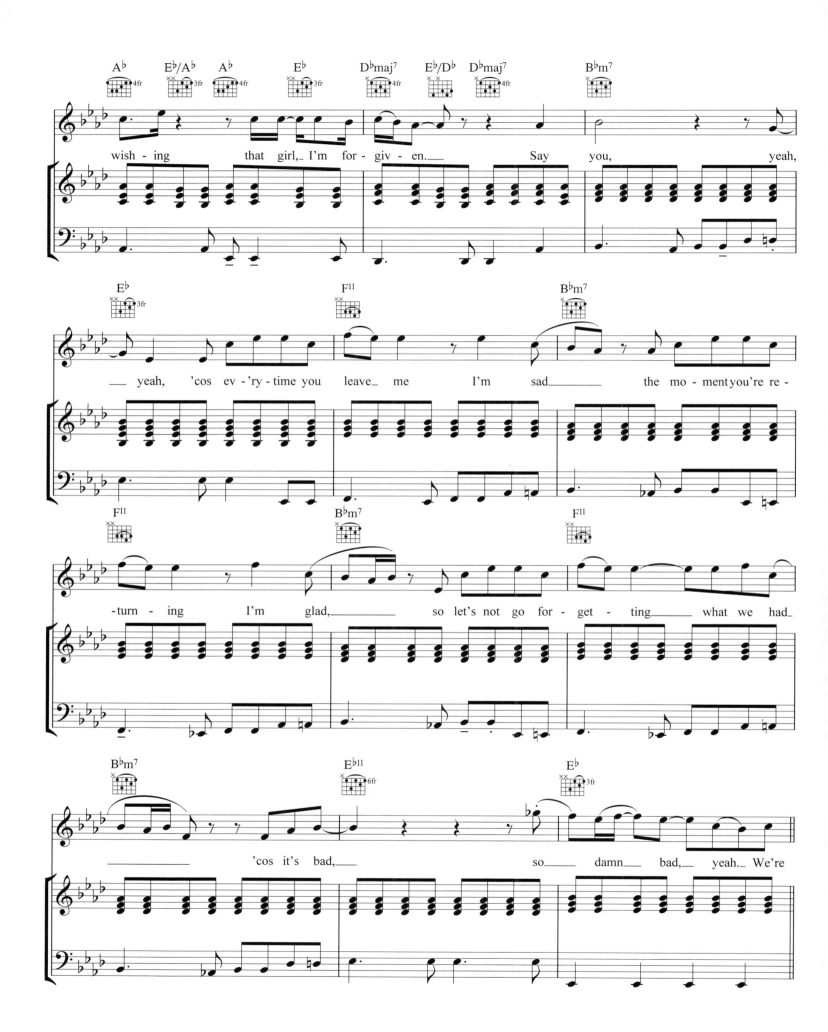

88

Verse 2:
If I hurt your feelings
Then baby we're even
'Cos I've been bereaving
Since you said you're leaving
But now you're by my side
Let's not fight 'cos you're right
That every time I lose you, I'm lost
No more 'you versus me' girl, there's just us
'Cos anything without you is just a bust
Baby trust, you must...

We're loving each day *etc.*

# Move Your Feet

Words & Music by Junior

stop. (Won't stop.) Won't stop the beat___ and go. Ooh.___

Bm⁷          Am⁷

Ev - 'ry - bo - dy,          move your feet___ and          feel u -

Bm⁷          **1, 2.**
              Am⁷

- ni - ted.          Oh.___
                                        (Ooh.)___

**3.**
Am

Yeah.

# Sun Is Shining

Words & Music by Bob Marley

know, y'all,                    where I stand.

(Mon-day morn-ing,)                here    I    am. __                        Want

you to know just if you can,         where I   stand.
(Tues-day eve-ning;)

(Wed'n-s'day morn-ing,) tell my-self a new day is ris-ing.

(Thurs-day eve-ning;) get on the rise, a new day is dawn-ing.

(Fri-day morn-ing,) here I am.

(Sat-ur-day eve-ning,) want you to know just, ___want you___ to know just where I stand. _

# Sunshine Day

Words & Music by Sol Amarfio, Teddy Osei & Michael Tontoh

smile will bring a sun-shine day.

108

# Twist And Shout

Words & Music by Bert Russell & Phil Medley

# Waiting For A Star To Fall

Words & Music by George Merrill & Shannon Rubicam

1. I hear your name whis - pered on the wind:___ it's a sound___
2. I've learned to feel what I can - not see,___ but with you___

that makes___ me___ cry.___ I hear a song blow a -
I lose___ that___ vi - sion.___ I don't know how to

-gain and a - gain___through my mind,___ and I don't___ know why.___
dream your dream, so I'm all___ caught up in the su - per - sti - tion.

-ting   makes me   love   you   ev - en   more.

*Instrumental*

Wait-

# What A Wonderful World

Words & Music by George Weiss & Bob Thiele

# Love Is In The Air

Words & Music by Harry Vanda & John Young

don't know if I feel__ sane;__ but it's some-thing__ that I must be-
don't know if I'm be-ing wise__ but it's some-thing__ that I must be-

-lieve in,__ and it's there when__ you call out__ my name.__
-lieve in,__ and it's there when__ I look in__ your eyes.__

Love is in__ the air,__